AS Chemistry

There's a big jump from GCSE to AS Chemistry.
And with modules to take as early as January, you need to
make sure you hit the ground running.

This book will give you a Head Start — it covers all those things that
trip you up when you move from GCSE to AS, and includes loads of
practice questions to make sure you've got the hang of it all.

Spend the first week of 6th form or (whisper it quietly) the summer holiday working
through it so everything will make perfect sense when you start your AS.

We've done our bit — the rest is up to you.

What CGP is all about

Our sole aim here at CGP is to produce the highest quality books
— carefully written, immaculately presented and dangerously
close to being funny.

Then we work our socks off to get them out to you
— at the cheapest possible prices.

Contents

Section One — The Structure of the Atom

Atomic Structure 1

Atomic Number, Mass Number and Isotopes 2

Relative Atomic Mass 3

The Mole 4

Arrangement of Electrons 5

Section Two — Chemical Bonds

Electronic Structure and the Periodic Table 6

Ionic Bonding 7

Covalent Bonding 8

Section Three — Ionic and Covalent Structures

Formation of Positive and Negative Ions 9

The Ionic Lattice 10

Physical Properties of Ionic Compounds 11

Questions on Ionic Structures 12

Small Covalent Molecules 13

Giant Covalent Structures 15

Trends in Properties Across the Periodic Table 17

Section Four — Hydrocarbon Molecules

Fractional Distillation of Crude Oil 19

Combustion of Hydrocarbons 20

Alkanes 21

Alkenes 22

Section Five — Rates of Reaction

Reaction Rates 24

Reaction Rates and Catalysts 25

Section Six — Reversible Reactions

Reversible Reactions.. 26

Influence of Conditions on Yield 27

Section Seven — Symbol Equations

Formulae of Compounds 29
Writing and Balancing Equations 30

Section Eight — Calculating Formulae

Determination of Formulae from Reacting Masses 32
Calculation of Empirical Formulae 33
Determination of Formulae from Reacting Masses 34

Section Nine — The Periodic Table

Making Use of the Periodic Table 35

Section Ten — Reactivity and the Periodic Table

Reactivity and Group 2 37
Reactivity and Group 7 38
Reactivity Trends in Groups 2 and 7 39

Section Eleven — Chemical Reactions

Reaction Types 40

Section Twelve — Energy and Chemistry

Exothermic and Endothermic Reactions 43
Calculations Involving Making and Breaking Bonds 44

Section Thirteen — How Science Works

Evaluating Data 46

Index 48

Published by Coordination Group Publications Ltd.

Author:
David Mason

Editors:
Mary Falkner, Paul Jordin, Sharon Keeley, Julie Schofield

Proofread by:
Glenn Rogers

ISBN: 978 1 84762 116 0
Groovy website: www.cgpbooks.co.uk
Jolly bits of clipart from CorelDRAW®
Printed by Elanders Hindson Ltd, Newcastle upon Tyne.
Text, design, layout and original illustrations

Atomic Structure

What Are Atoms Like?

1) All atoms have a nucleus at their centre containing <u>neutrons</u> and <u>protons</u>.

2) Almost all of the mass of the atom is contained in the nucleus which also has an overall <u>positive</u> charge.

3) The positive charge arises because each of the protons in the nucleus has a +1 charge.

4) The nucleus is <u>tiny</u> compared with the total volume occupied by the whole atom.

5) The neutrons in the nucleus have a very similar mass to the protons but they are <u>uncharged</u>.

6) The electrons orbit the nucleus in shells (or energy levels). The electrons are much smaller and lighter than either the neutrons or protons.

7) The volume occupied by the orbits of the electrons determines the size of the atom.

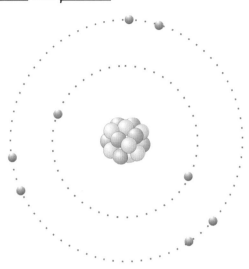

What is the Charge on an Atom?

The overall charge on an atom is <u>zero</u>.

This is because each +1 charge from a proton in the nucleus is cancelled out by a -1 charge from an electron.

If an atom loses or gains electrons it becomes <u>charged</u>. These charged particles are called <u>ions</u>. The fact that the protons and electrons are oppositely charged also helps to explain why the electrons remain in orbit: opposites attract.

Have a go at these questions:

1) Copy and complete the table:

Particle	Relative Mass	Relative Charge
Proton	1	
Neutron		
Electron	1/1840	

2) What is the charge on an ion formed when an atom loses two electrons?
3) What is the charge on an ion formed when an atom gains two electrons?

Answers

1)

Particle	Relative Mass	Relative Charge
Proton	1	+1
Neutron	1	0
Electron	1/1840	–1

2) +2
3) –2

Atomic Number, Mass Number and Isotopes

Atomic and Mass Numbers

The <u>atomic number</u> of an element is given the symbol Z.
It is sometimes called the <u>proton number</u> as it represents the number of protons in the nucleus of the element.
For atoms the number of protons equals the number of electrons, but you need to take care when considering ions as the number of electrons changes when an ion forms from an atom.

The <u>mass number</u> of an atom is given the symbol A. It represents the total number of neutrons and protons in the nucleus. Subtracting Z from A allows you to calculate the number of neutrons in the nucleus.

Try this question (you may need to refer to the Periodic Table on page 6):

1)   Copy and complete the table:

Element	Symbol	Z	A	No. Protons	No. Neutrons	No. Electrons
Sodium			23			
		6	12			
		12			12	
		84	210			
Chlorine		17	35			
Chlorine		17	37			

Isotopes

The last two examples in the table above show two chlorine atoms with different numbers of neutrons. These are called <u>isotopes</u> of chlorine. Both are chlorine atoms because they have the same number of protons — but they have different numbers of neutrons. In other words they have the same atomic number but different mass numbers. Isotopes are very common: some occur naturally and some are man-made. Some elements may have a large number of isotopes.

Have a go at these questions:

2)   In terms of the numbers of subatomic particles, state one difference and two similarities between two isotopes of the same element.
3)   Give the chemical symbol, mass number and atomic number of an atom which has 3 electrons and 4 neutrons.
4)   Three isotopes of carbon are: carbon-12, carbon-13 and carbon-14. State the numbers of protons, neutrons and electrons in each.

Relative Atomic Mass

Calculating the Relative Atomic Mass

When you look up the mass number of an element on a detailed copy of the Periodic Table, you'll see that it isn't always a _whole number_. This is because the value given is the _average mass number_ for two or more isotopes. This is further complicated by the fact that some isotopes are more _abundant_ than others. The average mass number of an element is called its _relative atomic mass_, or A_r.

In a sample of chlorine there are on average 3 atoms with mass number 35 to every atom with mass number 37. So the relative atomic mass of chlorine is 35.5.

How can we calculate the average mass number for a number of isotopes?

Example: Find the relative atomic mass of chlorine.

	chlorine-35		chlorine-37
Ratio of atoms	3	:	1
Relative abundance	¾		¼

Average mass = abundance of Cl-35 × 35 + abundance of Cl-37 × 37
$\quad$ = ¾ × 35 + ¼ × 37
$\quad$ = 26.25 + 9.25
$\quad$ = 35.5

Note: the _relative abundance_ is arrived at by considering that 3 out of every 4 (¾) atoms will be Cl-35, and 1 out of 4 (¼) will be Cl-37.

Now have a go at these:

1) Find the relative atomic mass of magnesium if there is 1 atom of Mg-24 to every atom of Mg-25.
2) Find the relative atomic mass of carbon if there are 99 atoms of C-12 to every atom of C-13.
3) Find the relative atomic mass of argon if there are 16 atoms of Ar-40 to every 3 atoms of Ar-39.

If you add up the relative atomic masses of all the atoms in a chemical formula, you get the _relative formula mass_, or M_r, of that compound.

For example: $\quad$ Relative formula mass of $CaCl_2$ = (1 × 40) + (2 × 35.5) = 111

(If the compound is molecular, you might hear the term _relative molecular mass_ used instead, but it means pretty much the same.)

Try these calculations (you may need to refer to the Periodic Table on page 6):

4) Find the relative formula mass of sodium fluoride, NaF.
5) Find the relative formula mass of chloromethane, CH_3Cl.

Answers
1) 24.5
2) 12.01
3) 39.84
4) 42
5) 50.5

The Mole

A Mole is a Number of Particles

If you wanted to count the number of atoms that you had in a sample of a substance, you'd have to use some very big numbers, and spend a very long time counting. So you need a unit to describe the amount of a substance that you have — that unit is the mole.

One mole of a substance contains 6.02×10^{23} particles.
6.02×10^{23} mol^{-1} is known as Avogadro's number.

The particles can be anything — e.g. atoms or molecules.
So 6.02×10^{23} atoms of carbon is 1 mole of carbon,
and 6.02×10^{23} molecules of CO_2 is 1 mole of CO_2.

No, I'm not getting on there. That joke's far too obvious...

Molar Mass is the Mass of One Mole

One mole of atoms or molecules has a mass in grams equal to the relative formula mass (A_r or M_r) of that substance.

Carbon has an A_r of 12 $\longrightarrow$ 1 mole of carbon weighs 12 g $\longrightarrow$ The molar mass of carbon is 12 g/mol
CO_2 has an M_r of 44 $\longrightarrow$ 1 mole of CO_2 weighs 44 g $\longrightarrow$ The molar mass of CO_2 is 44 g/mol

So you know that 12 g of carbon and 44 g of CO_2 must contain the same number of particles.

You can use molar mass in calculations to work out how many moles of a substance you have.

Just use this formula:
$$\text{Number of moles} = \frac{\text{Mass of substance (g)}}{\text{Molar mass (g/mol)}}$$

Example: How many moles of sodium oxide are present in 24.8g of Na_2O?

Molar mass of Na_2O $= (2 \times 23) + (1 \times 16) = 62$ g/mol
Number of moles of Na_2O $= 24.8$ g $\div 62$ g/mol
$= 0.4$ moles

Use the Periodic Table on page 6 to help you answer these questions:

1) Find the molar mass of zinc.
2) Find the molar mass of sulfuric acid, H_2SO_4.
3) How many moles of sodium chloride are present in 117 g of NaCl?
4) I have 54 g of water (H_2O) and 84 g of iron (Fe).
Do I have more moles of water or of iron?

Answers
1) 65 g/mol
2) 98 g/mol
3) 2 moles
4) I have more moles of water (54 g = 3 moles H_2O, 84 g = 1.5 moles Fe)

Arrangement of Electrons

Electrons are Arranged in Energy Levels

Electrons orbit the nucleus in _energy levels_ (also called _shells_).

The first energy level can contain up to 2 electrons. It is called an _'s' level_.
The second energy level can contain up to 8 electrons. However it is actually split into
2 sub-levels. Two of the electrons are in an 's' level and the remaining 6 are in a _'p' level_.

At GCSE the 's' and 'p' sub-levels are not distinguished. You simply combine the 2 's' electrons
with the 6 'p' electrons to make a total of 8.

How can Electron Arrangements be Represented?

You can draw _concentric circles_ to represent the different energy levels.
Then add crosses to represent the electrons at each level.

For an atom with 20 electrons:

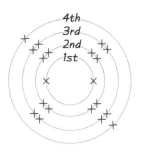

The diagram on the left shows the
energy levels filling up with electrons.

Remember you should always start
filling the _innermost_ levels first.

Here's another way to show electron arrangements:

An atom with 6 electrons: 2, 4
An atom with 11 electrons: 2, 8, 1
An atom with 20 electrons: 2, 8, 8, 2

Use the Periodic Table on page 6 to help you answer the following questions:

1) Draw diagrams to show the electron arrangements of the following elements:
   carbon, fluorine, magnesium, sulfur
2) Write the electron arrangements of the following elements using the format shown above:
   lithium, sodium, potassium, beryllium, magnesium, calcium

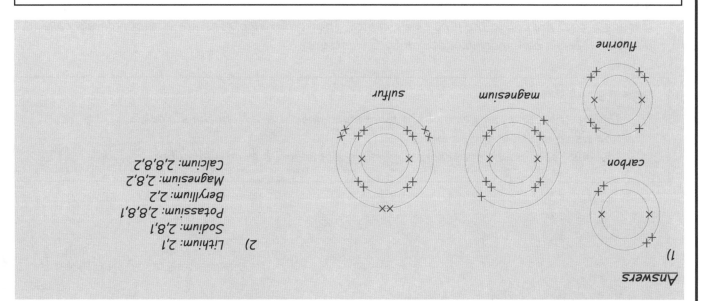

Answers

2) Lithium: 2,1
    Sodium: 2,8,1
    Potassium: 2,8,8,1
    Beryllium: 2,2
    Magnesium: 2,8,2
    Calcium: 2,8,8,2

1)

Electronic Structure and the Periodic Table

The Periodic Table

The Periodic Table contains:

- All of the elements in order of atomic number
- Metallic elements on the left-hand side
- Vertical <u>groups</u> of elements which have similar properties
- Horizontal rows of elements called <u>periods</u>

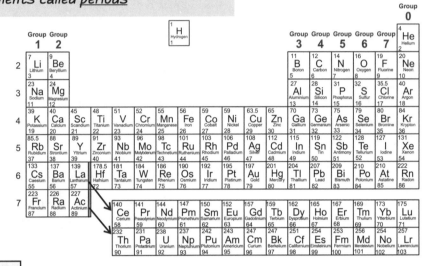

What Are Groups?

Chemical reactions involve atoms reacting to gain a <u>full outer shell</u> of electrons.

All of the elements in a group have the same number of electrons in their outer shell.

As a result, the elements in a group react in a similar way.

The Periodic Table is Split into Blocks

As well as being split into groups and periods, the Periodic Table has four <u>blocks</u>. You only need to worry about two of them at the moment though — the <u>'s' block</u> and the <u>'p' block</u>.

<u>Groups 1 and 2</u> are called the s-block elements. Their outer electrons are in energy levels called s levels. S levels can accommodate up to 2 electrons.

<u>Groups 3 to 0</u> are called the p-block elements. Their outer electrons are in energy levels called p levels. P levels can accommodate up to 6 electrons.

Have a go at this question:

1) Draw a table showing which of the following elements are from the s block, and which are from the p block:
   caesium, potassium, phosphorus, calcium, aluminium, barium and sulfur.

Ionic Bonding

Reaction Between Group 1 and Group 7 Elements

Elements in Groups 1, 2, 6 and 7 react to form _ionic_ compounds.

Example: Sodium reacting with chlorine to form sodium chloride.

Sodium atom gives up outer electron to become a Na⁺ ion.

The positively charged Na⁺ ion is attracted to the negatively charged Cl⁻ ion, forming an ionic bond.

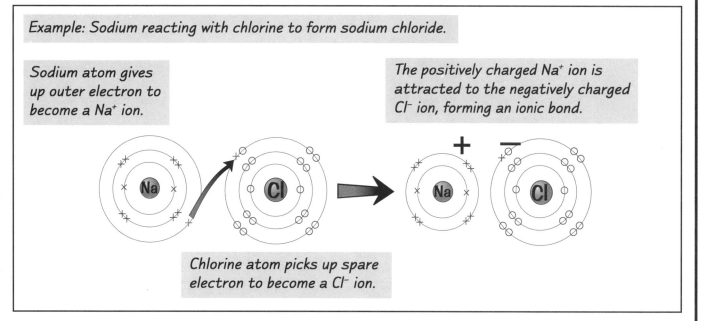

Chlorine atom picks up spare electron to become a Cl⁻ ion.

The example shows a typical reaction between a Group 1 element and a Group 7 element.
The sodium atom donates its single outer electron to the outer shell of the chlorine atom.
As a result, both elements end up with a full outer shell of electrons.
In a similar way, Group 2 elements react by donating two electrons and Group 6 elements react by gaining two electrons.

Have a go at these:

1) Draw a diagram showing how a magnesium atom reacts with an oxygen atom.
   In your diagram try to clearly demonstrate the electron transfer process.
2) Draw a diagram showing the electron transfer process that results in the formation of
   calcium chloride ($CaCl_2$).

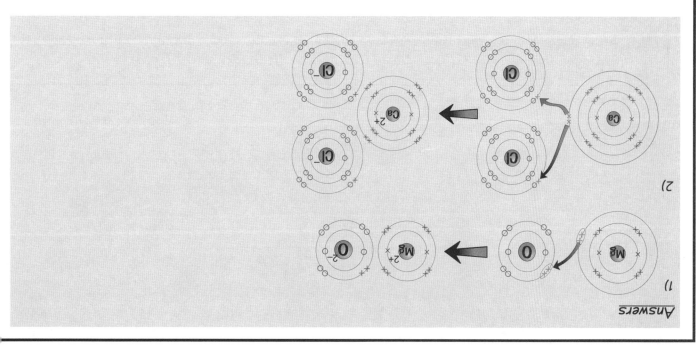

Answers

Covalent Bonding

Reaction Between Carbon and Hydrogen

Ionic bonding only really works between metals with one or two electrons in their outer shell, and non-metals that are one or two electrons short of a full outer shell. Elements with half-full shells have to do something different.

The diagrams below show two such atoms: <u>carbon and hydrogen</u>

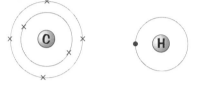

These elements do not gain or lose electrons. They <u>share</u> their electrons rather than transferring them. This results in the formation of <u>covalent bonds</u>. A covalent bond is a shared pair of electrons. When a small number of atoms share electrons in this way a small covalent molecule results. Such molecules can be represented in several different ways:

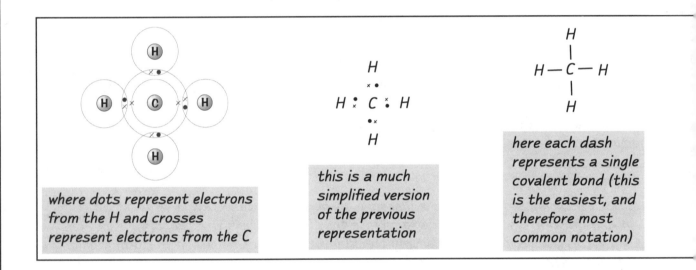

where dots represent electrons from the H and crosses represent electrons from the C

this is a much simplified version of the previous representation

here each dash represents a single covalent bond (this is the easiest, and therefore most common notation)

Try this question:

1) Draw 'dot and cross' diagrams showing the shared electron pairs in the following molecules: hydrogen (H_2), chlorine (Cl_2), ammonia (NH_3), water (H_2O), oxygen (O_2), ethane (C_2H_6).

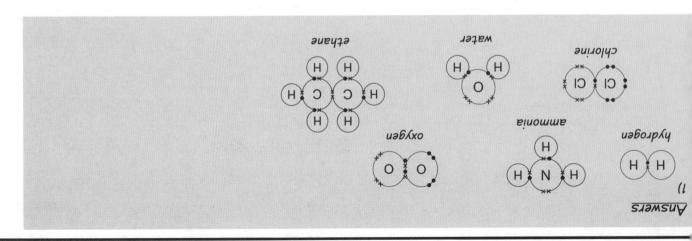

ethane

water

chlorine

oxygen

ammonia

hydrogen

1)

Formation of Positive and Negative Ions

Elements in Groups 1, 2, 6 and 7 form Simple Ions

The elements that form ions most readily are those in _Groups 1 and 2_ (which form positive ions, or _cations_), and in _Groups 6 and 7_ (which form negative ions, or _anions_).
Elements in these four groups all form ions with _noble gas electronic structures_.
It's fairly easy to work out the charges on these ions — follow through the reasoning below:

Group 1 atoms have one electron in their outer shell. The easiest way for them to achieve a full outer shell is to _lose_ that one negative electron. The positive charge in the nucleus stays the same leaving one excess positive charge overall, so _Group 1 ions must have a +1 charge_.

Group 2 atoms have two electrons in their outer shell. They _lose_ these two negative electrons to get a stable (full) outer shell, producing _ions with a +2 charge_.

Group 6 elements have six electrons in their outer shell. Rather than releasing all six of these electrons (which would take a lot of energy) they _pick up_ two electrons from their surroundings to complete their outer shell. The positive charge in the nucleus stays the same, so _Group 6 ions have two extra negative charges — they carry a –2 charge_.

Group 7 atoms need to _pick up_ one extra electron to get a stable outer shell, so they _form ions with a charge of –1_.

Not all Ions are as Simple

Some _groups of atoms_ can also exist as stable ions. These are usually _anions_ (negative ions) like sulfate and carbonate (one of the few exceptions being ammonium with a +1 charge). It is harder to work out the charges on these than in the case of the simple ions above. (To be able to work them out reliably, you need to know a bit of chemistry called the '_electronegativity series_', which I won't go into here.)

It is useful to _learn_ the charges on the most common of these molecular ions:

+1	-2	-1
NH_4^+ (ammonium)	SO_4^{2-} (sulfate)	OH^- (hydroxide)
	CO_3^{2-} (carbonate)	NO_3^- (nitrate)
	SO_3^{2-} (sulfite)	HCO_3^- (hydrogencarbonate)
		CN^- (cyanide)

Transition metals (the block of elements between _Groups 2 and 3_) also form ions. They are positive (like all metal ions) but they do not form ions with a noble gas electronic structure. This means that you cannot predict the charges in the same way as you can with the s-block metals.

Also, most transition metals can form more than one ion. The different charges are called '_oxidation states_' of the element. The most common ones that you should be aware of are:

$$Fe^{2+}, Fe^{3+}, Cu^{2+}, Co^{2+}, Ni^{2+}, Zn^{2+} \text{ and } Cr^{3+}$$

These ions tend to be _coloured_.

The Ionic Lattice

Ionic Bonds Produce Giant Ionic Structures

Unlike covalent bonds, ionic bonds do not work in any particular _direction_. The electromagnetic attraction is just as strong in all directions around the ion.

This means that when ionic compounds form, they produce _giant lattices_.

The lattice is a _closely packed_ regular array of ions, with each negative ion surrounded by positive ions and vice versa. The forces between the oppositely charged ions are _very strong_.

Sodium chloride forms a lattice like this one. This is called the _sodium chloride structure_.

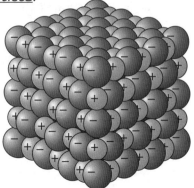

If you look closely at the individual crystals of table salt (sodium chloride) you can see that they tend to be cuboid in shape. This is because each crystal is one giant ionic lattice.

You Can Find The Ratio of Positive to Negative Ions

The ratio of positive ions to negative ions in a crystal depends on the charges of the ions.
Look closely at the diagram of the sodium chloride structure. You'll see that the sodium (Na^+) ions and chloride (Cl^-) ions alternate — for each sodium ion there's one chloride ion. So the ratio of sodium ions to chloride ions in a crystal of sodium chloride is 1:1.

The number of _positive_ charges in the lattice must be _equal_ to the number of _negative_ charges in the lattice to make it _electrically neutral_.

Example: The calcium chloride lattice

The ionic compound calcium chloride is made up of Ca^{2+} ions and Cl^- ions.
For the lattice to be electrically neutral it must contain two Cl^- ions (2 × −1) to balance the charge of each Ca^{2+} ion (1 × +2). So the ratio of Ca^{2+} ions to Cl^- ions in the crystal must be 1:2.

Now try these questions:

1) In a copper(II) oxide crystal, what is the ratio of Cu^{2+} ions to O^{2-} ions?
2) In a sodium oxide crystal, what is the ratio of Na^+ ions to O^{2-} ions?

Ionic Bond Strength Depends on the Charge on the Ions

The strength of the bonds between ions is not the same in all ionic structures:

The _bigger the charges_ on the ions, the _stronger the attraction_.

So, for example, the bonds between the ions in MgO ($Mg^{2+}O^{2-}$) will be stronger than those between the ions in NaCl (Na^+Cl^-).

Physical Properties of Ionic Compounds

Melting Points

In order to melt a solid, the forces holding the particles _rigidly within the lattice_ structure have to be overcome. In an ionic solid, these bonds are very strong, so a large amount of energy is required to break them. So:

Ionic compounds have very high melting points.

The melting points and boiling points of ionic compounds are often about on a par with those of covalent macromolecular compounds (see page 15).

Solubility

In many cases ionic compounds are soluble in water.

This happens because water is a _polar molecule_. The oxygen end is slightly negative and is attracted to the positive ions, while the hydrogen end is slightly positive and is attracted to the negative ions.

Although lots of energy is required to break the strong bonds within the lattice, it is provided by the formation of many weak bonds between the water molecules and the ions in solution.

The diagram below shows a crystal of sodium chloride dissolving in a beaker of water.

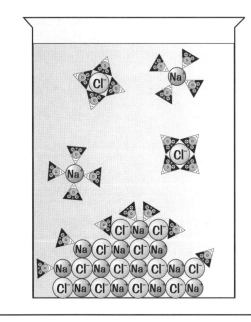

This is a simple representation of a water molecule

The water molecules surround the ions in solution. The positive end of the molecule points towards negative ions and the negative end towards positive ions.

As you can see from the diagram, the crystal does not dissolve instantly, but rather is slowly broken up.

Electrical Conductivity

In their solid form, ionic compounds are _electrical insulators_. They have no free ions or electrons to carry electric current.

However, when _molten or dissolved_, the ions separate and are free to move. This allows the substance to _conduct electricity_.

All ionic compounds conduct electricity when molten or dissolved.

Questions on Ionic Structures

Have a go at these questions on ionic structures:

1) Using the Periodic Table on page 6, predict the charge on, and write the symbol for, the ion formed from each of the following elements:
   a) Aluminium
   b) Barium
   c) Rubidium
   d) Phosphorus
   e) Bromine
   f) Selenium
   g) Strontium

2) Give two reasons why it would be difficult to answer the question above for one of the transition metals, e.g. iron.

3) In a calcium fluoride crystal, what is the ratio of Ca^{2+} ions to F^- ions?

4) Put the following ionic compounds in order of melting point, highest to lowest:
   Lithium oxide (Li_2O), Beryllium oxide (BeO), Lithium fluoride (LiF)
   Explain why you have put them in that order.
   (You might want to use the Periodic Table on page 6 for this question.)

1) a) Al^{3+}
   b) Ba^{2+}
   c) Rb^+
   d) P^{3-}
   e) Br^-
   f) Se^{2-}
   g) Sr^{2+}

2) Transition metals do not form ions with noble gas electronic structures, which makes it difficult to predict the charges on them.
   Many transition metals (including iron) can form more than one ion — they have more than one possible oxidation state.

3) 1:2

4) BeO, Li_2O, LiF
   The higher the charges on the ions, the stronger the bonds between them. The stronger the bonds, the higher the melting point. Beryllium oxide is formed from ions which both have charges of magnitude 2. Lithium oxide is formed from oxide ions with a −2 charge and lithium ions with only a +1 charge. The ions in lithium fluoride both have charges of magnitude 1. Therefore the strongest bonds will be in beryllium oxide, followed by lithium oxide, then lithium fluoride.

Small Covalent Molecules

Hydrocarbons

Good examples of small covalent molecules are the <u>hydrocarbons</u> — the simplest examples of which are <u>alkanes</u>. These form a large 'family' of molecules each containing <u>carbon and hydrogen atoms</u> sharing electrons. The first four members of the family are shown below:

$$H-\underset{\underset{H}{|}}{\overset{\overset{H}{|}}{C}}-H \qquad H-\underset{\underset{H}{|}}{\overset{\overset{H}{|}}{C}}-\underset{\underset{H}{|}}{\overset{\overset{H}{|}}{C}}-H \qquad H-\underset{\underset{H}{|}}{\overset{\overset{H}{|}}{C}}-\underset{\underset{H}{|}}{\overset{\overset{H}{|}}{C}}-\underset{\underset{H}{|}}{\overset{\overset{H}{|}}{C}}-H \qquad H-\underset{\underset{H}{|}}{\overset{\overset{H}{|}}{C}}-\underset{\underset{H}{|}}{\overset{\overset{H}{|}}{C}}-\underset{\underset{H}{|}}{\overset{\overset{H}{|}}{C}}-\underset{\underset{H}{|}}{\overset{\overset{H}{|}}{C}}-H$$

methane   ethane   propane   butane

> The boiling points of these four alkanes are:
>
> | Alkane: | Methane | Ethane | Propane | Butane |
> |---|---|---|---|---|
> | B.p. °C: | -161 | -89 | -42 | 0 |

There is a clear trend showing that as the molecules get larger their boiling point increases. This is mainly due to the fact that the larger molecules have a greater surface area over which attractive forces can act.

Have a go at this question:

1) Use the data above to predict the boiling points of the next four members of the alkane series. They are called pentane, hexane, heptane and octane. (Bear in mind that, in chemistry, the first member of a series does not always provide an ideal example.)

Other Factors Affecting Boiling Point

If you substitute a chlorine atom for one of the hydrogen atoms in a methane molecule, this has a marked effect on the boiling point.

> Boiling point of methane (CH_4)   = -161 °C.
> Boiling point of chloromethane (CH_3Cl) = -24 °C.

The reason for the dramatic increase in boiling point is that the chlorine atom <u>polarises</u> the molecule, making one end slightly positive and the other slightly negative. The oppositely charged ends of different molecules attract each other, so more energy is required to separate them. This results in an increase in boiling point.

Small Covalent Molecules

More Complex Small Covalent Molecules

You've already had some practice at drawing some examples of small covalent molecules on page 8. You may have noticed that not all of the electron pairs around the central atom are bonding electrons. In other words, not all of the electrons are shared between the atoms in the molecule.

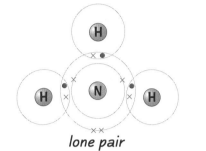

lone pair

In the diagram of <u>ammonia</u> (NH_3) on the left you can see that there are 4 electron pairs around the central nitrogen atom. Three of these electron pairs are called <u>bonding pairs</u> as they are shared between the nitrogen and hydrogen atoms.
The fourth electron pair is not shared between the atoms in the molecule. This is called a <u>lone pair</u>.

Effect of Lone Pairs on Boiling Points

Small molecules that have both a lone pair of electrons and one or more hydrogen atoms are attracted together quite strongly. This is because the hydrogen atoms of one molecule are attracted to the lone pair of electrons in a different molecule. This is called a <u>hydrogen bond</u>.

The strength of this attraction is greater than that between either non-polar molecules (e.g. hydrocarbons) or polar molecules. It is, in fact, the strongest <u>intermolecular</u> attraction, though it is not as strong as either an ionic or a covalent bond.

Try this question:

1) Draw a diagram showing three water molecules attracted together. You should use dotted lines to indicate forces between atoms in different molecules. (Hint: think about where the lone pairs will be on a water molecule.)

Other Properties of Small Covalent Molecules

Solubility

Small covalent molecules that are <u>not polar</u> at all (e.g. hydrocarbons) don't mix well with water, or dissolve very well in it. This is because the attractive force that exists between two water molecules is much stronger than that between a water molecule and a hydrocarbon molecule. So a mixture of a hydrocarbon and water will separate into two layers after shaking.

Electrical Conductivity

Small covalent molecules do not contain any of the free charged particles that are needed to carry an electric current. As a result they cannot conduct electricity — they are <u>electrical insulators</u>.

1)

Answers

Giant Covalent Structures

Giant Covalent Structures

On page 8 you saw that <u>carbon</u> is ideally placed to share electrons and form covalent bonds, because it has a half-full outer shell. Carbon atoms can share their electrons without involving any other elements. This can result in the formation of a single massive carbon molecule — a <u>macromolecule</u>.

Carbon can form various different giant structures such as <u>diamond and graphite</u>.
<u>Silicon dioxide</u> (which sand is made of) is another example of a giant covalent structure.

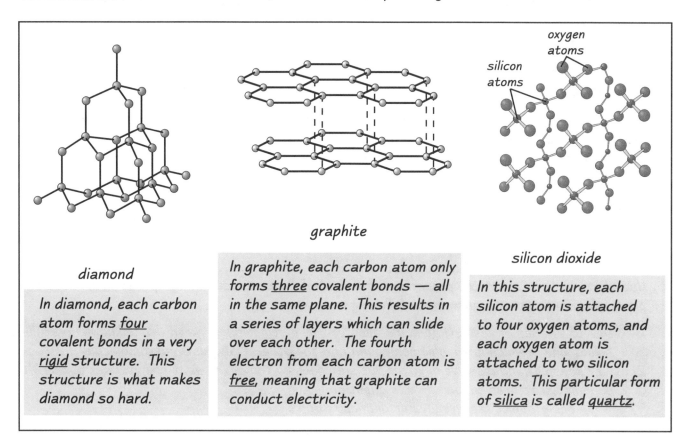

oxygen
atoms

silicon
atoms

graphite

diamond

silicon dioxide

In diamond, each carbon atom forms <u>four</u> covalent bonds in a very <u>rigid</u> structure. This structure is what makes diamond so hard.

In graphite, each carbon atom only forms <u>three</u> covalent bonds — all in the same plane. This results in a series of layers which can slide over each other. The fourth electron from each carbon atom is <u>free</u>, meaning that graphite can conduct electricity.

In this structure, each silicon atom is attached to four oxygen atoms, and each oxygen atom is attached to two silicon atoms. This particular form of <u>silica</u> is called <u>quartz</u>.

Melting and Boiling Points

Covalent macromolecules have very different physical properties from small molecules.

Unlike small molecules, melting points are extremely high, as all of the millions of covalent bonds need to be broken in order to allow the atoms within the structure to move freely.

This contrasts with small molecules where no covalent bonds need to be broken in order to separate the molecules.

	Melting point (°C)	Boiling point (°C)
Diamond	3550	4830
Quartz	1650	2230
Water	0	100
Methane	-182	-161

Just to get an idea of the scale of the difference, compare the melting points and boiling points of <u>diamond and quartz</u> with those of <u>water and methane</u>.

Giant Covalent Structures

Electrical Conductivity

Covalent macromolecules are <u>electrical insulators</u>.

Both the lack of charged particles and the freedom for them to move results in macromolecules being electrical insulators. Even a molten covalent compound will not conduct electricity. <u>Graphite</u> is the only exception to this rule, as the loosely held electrons between the layers of atoms can move through the solid structure. Graphite conducts in both its solid and liquid forms.

Solubility

Covalent macromolecules are <u>not soluble in water</u>.

A similar argument to that for their high boiling points applies here. To get a macromolecule to dissolve, all the covalent bonds joining the atoms together need to be broken. There is no way to get the energy required to do this, since the individual neutral particles in the structure will not form intermolecular bonds with the water molecules.

(Compare this with the solubility of the giant ionic lattice on p11.)

Use what you know about the properties of giant molecular structures compared with those of giant ionic structures to answer the following questions:

1) Devise a series of tests that would allow you to distinguish between two unknown crystalline solids, one of which is an ionic compound and the other a covalent macromolecule.
2) Why doesn't sand dissolve in water but salt does? (You might want to look back at the bits on ionic structures to answer this question.)
3) Why does graphite feel greasy but diamonds don't?

Answers

1) You could use solubility, though not all ionic compounds are soluble in water so this test may prove inconclusive. Melt and check to see if the molten substance conducts — if it does it's probably ionic. You need to be careful of graphite though, which is a macromolecular conductor. To get around this, you could test the conductivity of the crystal in its solid form as well. While solid graphite will conduct, ionic salts only conduct electricity in the molten state (or in solution).

2) In salt, the energy required to break the strong ionic bonds is provided when the ions become surrounded by water molecules. Fewer strong bonds are replaced by many more weaker bonds. In the case of a covalent macromolecule there is no way to get the energy required to break the many strong covalent bonds. As a result the bonds don't break so the sand doesn't dissolve.

3) In graphite the layers of carbon atoms can slide over each other making it feel greasy. In the case of diamond the rigid structure prevents any movement.

Trends in Properties Across the Periodic Table

Structure and Bonding Change Across the Periodic Table

You should have seen from this section how much the properties of a compound depend on its bonding and structure. You also know that the type of bonding that occurs depends on the number of electrons in the outer shells of the elements making up the compound, and so their positions in the Periodic Table.

A good way to compare the way that different elements bond is by looking at the properties of a series of similar _compounds_ across a period.
Look at the information in the table below about all the _Period 3 oxides_. You can see that there are clear _patterns_ in the data.

Trends Across Period Three

(Period 3 is studied because it is a _simple case_.
There are no _transition metals_ to confuse matters.)

The table below shows some of the physical properties of Period 3 oxides.
The final row has been deduced from these physical properties.

	Na_2O	MgO	Al_2O_3	SiO_2	P_4O_{10}	SO_2
State (at room temperature and standard pressure)	solid	solid	solid	solid	solid	gas
Melting point (°C) (at standard pressure)	1275	2800	2072	1650	570	–73
Electrical conductivity (when molten)	good	good	good	none	none	none
Bonding	ionic lattice	ionic lattice	ionic lattice	covalent macromolecule	small covalent molecule	small covalent molecule

[Chlorine and argon do not react with oxygen.]

You can see from this data that there is a change in the properties of the Period 3 oxides as you move from left to right across the Periodic Table.

The trend is from ionic bonding to small covalent molecules via a covalent macromolecule.

These trends across a period are more _subtle_ than the trends going down a group that you saw at GCSE. However they are extremely useful as they allow you to make predictions about the reactions and properties of unknown compounds. There are of course _exceptions_ to the rules/trends, but on the whole they allow links between physical properties and atomic structure to be made.

Trends in Properties Across the Periodic Table

Use the table on page 17 to help you answer the following questions:

1) Explain how the data in the first three rows of the table supports the idea that the bonding type changes from ionic to covalent as you move across Period 3.

2) Use the information on Period 3 <u>oxides</u> to predict the trend in the melting points of the <u>elements</u> as you go across Period 3.

3) What type of bonding would you expect the <u>chlorides</u> of sodium and magnesium to exhibit?

4) What type of bonding would you expect the chloride of phosphorus to exhibit?

5) How do you think the melting point of $MgCl_2$ will compare with that of PCl_3?

Section Three — Ionic and Covalent Structures

Fractional Distillation of Crude Oil

Crude Oil is a Mixture of Hydrocarbon Molecules

Hydrocarbons are compounds that contain only carbon and hydrogen. Carbon is special in its ability to form long chains of atoms that are held together by <u>covalent bonds</u>. You saw on page 13 that the boiling points of hydrocarbons change as the length of the carbon chain increases.

This property is used to separate the fractions of hydrocarbons in crude oil in a process called <u>fractional distillation</u>.

Fractional Distillation

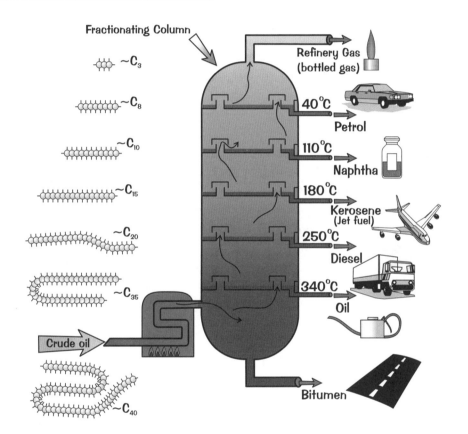

The <u>crude oil</u> is heated to about 350 °C and pumped into the <u>fractionating column</u>. A <u>temperature gradient</u> is maintained in the column (see the diagram). The vaporised hydrocarbons rise up the column until they reach the point where they condense. They are caught on layers in the columns and <u>tapped off</u>. The fractions are either used directly or processed further.

Have a go at these questions:

1) Which property is used to separate the fractions of crude oil?
2) What is the relationship between chain length and the temperature at which the hydrocarbon condenses?

Answers
1) boiling point
2) Longer chain length means higher temperature.

Combustion of Hydrocarbons

Combustion

Combustion is a type of _chemical reaction_ that involves a fuel reacting with oxygen to produce heat and light energy and waste products. _Hydrocarbons_ are used extensively as fuels (e.g. petrol, diesel, jet fuel, camping gas) and so combustion is a very important reaction. Combustion reactions give out heat — they are _exothermic_.

Complete Combustion — With Enough Oxygen

When a combustion reaction has a plentiful supply of oxygen the hydrocarbon undergoes complete combustion to give only two chemical products, _carbon dioxide_ and _water_.
The flame is usually a _faint blue_ colour.

e.g. $2C_2H_6(g) + 7O_2(g) \rightarrow 4CO_2(g) + 6H_2O(g)$ (+ energy)
ethane

Incomplete Combustion — Without Enough Oxygen

If combustion takes place without enough oxygen then among the products will be the highly poisonous gas _carbon monoxide_ and _carbon_ itself. The flame of this type of reaction is _yellow_ and can produce _sooty marks_.

hydrocarbon + oxygen $\rightarrow CO_2(g) + H_2O(g) + CO(g) + C(s)$ (+ energy)

Try these:

1) Write balanced symbol equations for the complete combustion of:
methane (CH_4), ethene (C_2H_4), butane (C_4H_{10}), hexene (C_6H_{12}).
2) Why is it important to make sure that gas fires and gas central heating units are burning the methane gas completely and are well ventilated?
3) Give an example of where incomplete combustion is used in a laboratory for safety reasons.

1) Methane: $CH_4(g) + 2O_2(g) \rightarrow CO_2(g) + 2H_2O(g)$
Ethene: $C_2H_4(g) + 3O_2(g) \rightarrow 2CO_2(g) + 2H_2O(g)$
Butane: $2C_4H_{10}(g) + 13O_2(g) \rightarrow 8CO_2(g) + 10H_2O(g)$ or $C_4H_{10}(g) + 6\frac{1}{2}O_2(g) \rightarrow 4CO_2(g) + 5H_2O(g)$
Hexene: $C_6H_{12}(l) + 9O_2(g) \rightarrow 6CO_2(g) + 6H_2O(g)$
2) Incomplete combustion would release carbon monoxide into the room, which is poisonous.
3) The yellow flame on a Bunsen burner is due to incomplete combustion (setting the burner to a yellow flame means you can clearly see that it's on).

Section Four — Hydrocarbon Molecules

Alkanes

Structure and Bonding in Alkanes

Alkanes contain two types of bond. All of the carbon-carbon bonds are single covalent bonds. All of the other bonds are carbon-hydrogen covalent bonds (which are always single).

All of the available bonds have been formed, so we call alkanes saturated molecules.

(Remember that carbon always forms four covalent bonds and hydrogen makes one covalent bond.)

The diagrams below show the structures of the first four straight-chain alkanes: methane, ethane, propane and butane.

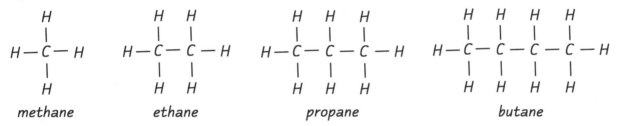

methane   ethane   propane   butane

It is important to realise that these structures are only 2D representations of the 3D molecules. The molecules are not rigid. There is free rotation around a carbon-carbon single bond. This means that the carbon chains are quite flexible and gives the molecules the ability to change shape, particularly as the chain length increases.

Properties of Alkanes

The bonds in alkanes are very strong and require a lot of energy to break them. This can be used to explain some of their properties:

1. They are very unreactive.
2. They are not able to form polymers.
3. They burn cleanly, tending to undergo complete combustion.

Also:

4. Boiling point increases as the length of the carbon chain increases.
5. Viscosity (resistance to flow) increases as chain length increases.
6. Volatility (ease of evaporation) decreases as chain length increases.

These last three properties are explained by the fact that the attractive forces between molecules get stronger as the chain length increases.

Try some questions:

1) Draw out the structures of the next two alkanes, pentane (C_5H_{12}) and hexane (C_6H_{14}).
2) We can work out a general formula for the alkanes of the form $C_nH_?$, where n is the number of carbon atoms. Work out what should be in place of the ?.

Answers

1) pentane

2) General Formula: C_nH_{2n+2}

Alkenes

Structure and Bonding in Alkenes

<u>Alkenes</u> are similar to alkanes in that they are also hydrocarbons. The difference is in the presence of a <u>carbon-carbon double covalent bond</u> (C=C) somewhere in the carbon chain.

This means that not all possible single bonds have been made; these molecules are <u>unsaturated</u>.

(As in all compounds the carbon atoms must have four bonds and hydrogen only one.)

The structures of the first three alkenes (ethene, propene and butene) are shown below:

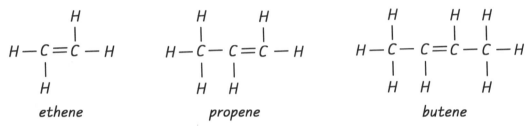

The presence of the C=C bond means that most alkenes have more than one possible structure. The C=C bond can be in various different positions along the chain.

Molecules with the same molecular formula but different structures are called <u>isomers</u>.

The C=C bond does not allow the same free rotation and flexibility around itself as a C–C bond. It is a rigid bond. But the rest of the carbon chain is the same as in an alkane molecule, so rotation is allowed around the single bonds.

Properties of Alkenes

The presence of the C=C bond dictates the chemical properties of alkenes.

1. They are <u>reactive</u> compounds, undergoing many different types of chemical reaction.
2. They <u>decolourise bromine water</u>. This is the standard test for alkenes.
3. They are used extensively to form <u>polymers</u>, e.g. poly(ethene).
4. They <u>do not burn cleanly</u>, giving very yellow flames and lots of soot.

Boiling point, viscosity and volatility follow the same trends as those of the alkanes.

Have a go at these:

1) Draw out a structure for the next alkene: pentene (C_5H_{10}).
2) Draw out two alternative structures for hexene (C_6H_{12}).
3) Work out the general formula for the alkenes of the form $C_nH_?$.

Answers

3) General formula: C_nH_{2n}

2) two of: [structures]

1) either: [structures]

Alkenes

Alkenes Can Form Polymers

The presence of the double bond in alkene molecules means that they are capable of forming _polymers_. A polymer is a long, chain-like molecule built up from lots of repeating units. In this case the repeating units, called _monomers_, are alkene molecules.

Under the right conditions (these depend on the alkene and the desired properties of the polymer), many small alkenes (like ethene and propene) will open up their double bonds and link together to form these long chain polymers.

The following example shows the formation of poly(ethene) (or _polythene_ for short):

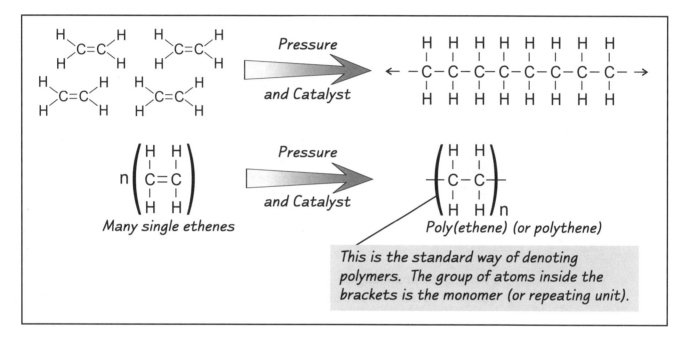

Many single ethenes

Poly(ethene) (or polythene)

This is the standard way of denoting polymers. The group of atoms inside the brackets is the monomer (or repeating unit).

Other Small Alkenes do a Similar Thing

Propene polymerises to form _polypropene_.

Styrene (which has a benzene ring in it — benzene is a ring of six carbon atoms in which the bonding electrons are shared between all six carbons) polymerises to form _polystyrene_.

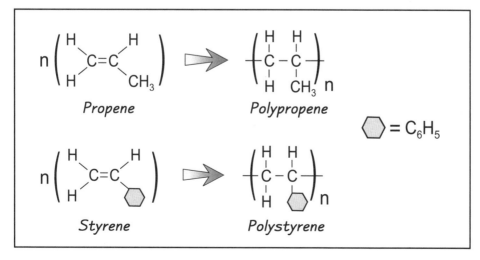

Propene

Polypropene

⬡ = C_6H_5

Styrene

Polystyrene

Reaction Rates

Measuring the Rate of a Reaction

The rate of reaction is just a measure of _how fast_ a particular reaction is going.

You need to know some of the ways that you can follow the rates of different reactions.

They're all about measuring how fast the _reactants_ are being _used up_, or measuring how fast the _products_ of the reaction are _forming_.

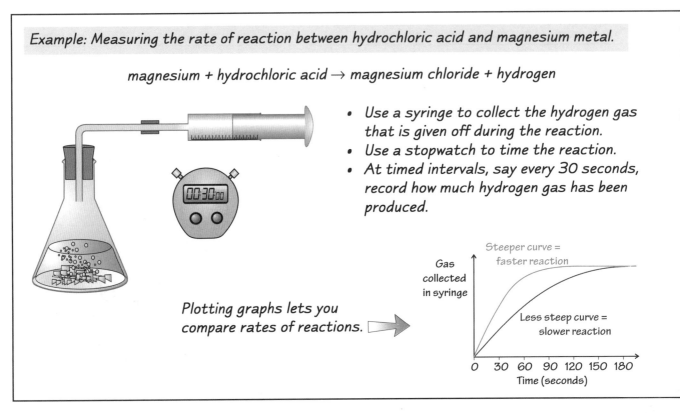

Example: Measuring the rate of reaction between hydrochloric acid and magnesium metal.

magnesium + hydrochloric acid → magnesium chloride + hydrogen

- Use a syringe to collect the hydrogen gas that is given off during the reaction.
- Use a stopwatch to time the reaction.
- At timed intervals, say every 30 seconds, record how much hydrogen gas has been produced.

Plotting graphs lets you compare rates of reactions.

Steeper curve = faster reaction

Gas collected in syringe

Less steep curve = slower reaction

0   30   60   90   120   150   180
Time (seconds)

There are lots of other ways of measuring the rate of a reaction:

1)   You can measure the _change in mass_ that occurs during a reaction where gas is released as one of the products.
 When solid calcium carbonate reacts with hydrochloric acid, carbon dioxide gas is released. If you mix the reactants in a flask and place the flask on a mass balance, you can record the decrease in mass as carbon dioxide is released.

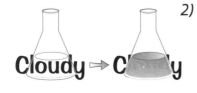

2)   You can follow the _colour change_ of a reaction. This includes _precipitation reactions_, where the solution turns cloudy as more of the product is made.
 If you mix sodium thiosulfate and hydrochloric acid, a precipitate of sulfur forms. Put a solid black mark on a piece of paper underneath the flask. Time how long it takes for the mark to be completely obscured.

3)   You can measure changes in _temperature_ or _pH_ that occur during the reaction.
 The reaction between sodium thiosulfate and hydrochloric acid is a neutralisation reaction. So you could also measure its rate by using a pH meter to track changes in pH.

Reaction Rates and Catalysts

Changing the Rate of Reaction

The rate of reaction depends on how often two particles <u>collide</u> with each other — the more collisions that occur between particles the <u>faster</u> the rate of reaction. But the particles also need to collide in the right direction and with <u>enough energy</u> or they won't react.

These factors all increase the rate of reaction:

1) <u>Increasing temperature</u> — the particles tend to have more kinetic energy. This means that they move around faster, and so are more likely to collide with each other <u>and</u> have enough energy to react.

2) <u>Increasing concentration (or pressure in gases)</u> — this means that the particles of reactant will be closer together, so they will be more likely to collide.

3) <u>Increasing the surface area of a solid reactant</u> — this increases the number of particles of the solid reactant able to come into contact with other reactants.

Catalysts Speed Up Reactions

<u>Activation energy</u> is the minimum amount of energy needed for a reaction to happen. This initial input of energy is needed to break bonds and start the reaction off.

A catalyst increases the rate of a reaction by <u>lowering its activation energy</u>. So catalysts can speed up reactions.

A <u>catalyst</u> is any substance which changes the <u>rate</u> of a reaction, without being <u>changed</u> or <u>used up</u> itself.

Catalysts are also very <u>specific</u> — most will only catalyse a single reaction.

There are loads of advantages to using catalysts:

1) Catalysts reduce the need for high temperatures and pressures in industrial reactions, like hydrocarbon cracking (see page 40) and ethanol production (see page 26). This makes these processes cheaper to run.

2) Using lower temperatures also means less energy demand, and so lower CO_2 emissions.

Living things produce <u>enzymes</u> which act as <u>biological catalysts</u>. Enzymes are protein molecules that speed up <u>useful chemical reactions</u> in the body.

Reversible Reactions

Reversible Reactions Go Both Ways

In a reversible reaction, the products can react with each other and change back into the reactants.

	Reactants				Products		
	A	+	B	⇌	C	+	D

So there are actually two reactions happening at once: $A + B \rightarrow C + D$ and $C + D \rightarrow A + B$.

Example: The industrial production of ethanol from ethene.

$$H_2C=CH_2(g) \; + \; H_2O(g) \; \underset{endothermic}{\overset{exothermic}{\rightleftharpoons}} \; CH_3CH_2OH(g)$$

Catalyst: H_3PO_4
Temperature: 300 °C
Pressure: 60 atm

Because the reaction is reversible you don't get a high yield — some of the ethanol converts back to ethene and water. But you can keep removing and recycling any ethene that you have left, so you can still end up with a good overall yield.

Reversible Reactions Reach an Equilibrium

If a reversible reaction is taking place in a _closed system_ it will eventually reach a state of _equilibrium_.

A _closed system_ is one where none of the reactants or products can escape.

1)   When a reaction begins there will be a high concentration of reactants, and a low concentration of products in the system.
     So the _forward_ reaction will be _fast_, and the _reverse_ reaction quite _slow_.

2)   The concentration of reactants will gradually decrease, while the products build up.
     So the forward reaction will start to slow down while the reverse reaction speeds up.

3)   After a while the forward reaction and the reverse reaction end up going at the _same rate_.
     From this point on the _concentration_ of the _reactants_ and _products won't change_.

4)   This is called _dynamic equilibrium_. The forward and reverse reactions are _both still happening_ — some reactant is being made into product, and some product is being made into reactant.

5)   But since these processes are going at _exactly the same rate_, it seems as if nothing's happening.

Influence of Conditions on Yield

Position of Equilibrium

The _position of equilibrium_ tells you the amount of reactants compared to the amount of products that are present when the reaction reaches an equilibrium.

Reactants   Products

$$A \ + \ B \ \rightleftharpoons \ C \ + \ D$$

If the position of equilibrium lies on the _left_-hand side, there are more reactants than products in the reaction mixture.

If the position of equilibrium lies on the _right_-hand side, there are more products than reactants in the reaction mixture.

Changing Conditions Changes the Equilibrium Position

Altering the conditions of a reversible reaction can move the position of equilibrium in one direction or the other. Careful control of the conditions can result in a _higher yield_ (more of the products).

Look at the production of _ethanol_ from _ethene_ again as an example:

$$H_2C{=}CH_2(g) \ + \ H_2O(g) \ \overset{\text{exothermic}}{\underset{\text{endothermic}}{\rightleftharpoons}} \ CH_3CH_2OH(g)$$

1. If you _increase the pressure_, conditions will favour the _forward reaction_ and ethanol (CH_3CH_2OH) will be formed. This is because two molecules of $H_2C{=}CH_2/H_2O$ react to form only one molecule of CH_3CH_2OH. This _reduces_ the pressure.
2. _Raising the temperature_ favours the _reverse reaction_. This is because it's _endothermic_ (see page 43) and absorbs the extra heat energy, _lowering_ the temperature.

These observations can be summarised by an important rule known as _Le Chatelier's Principle_:

"A reversible reaction will move its equilibrium position to resist any change in the conditions."

(Remember that altering the _pressure_ of a _gas_ is equivalent to altering the _concentration_ of a _solution_.)

Have a go at this question:

1) You are making ethanol from ethene and steam using the reaction shown above. What will happen to the yield of ethanol if you increase the amount of steam in the reaction mixture?

Answers

1) Increasing the amount of steam will increase the concentration of particles on the left of the equation (which will also increase the pressure on the left hand side), and move the position of equilibrium to the right, increasing the yield of ethanol.

Influence of Conditions on Yield

Deciding on the Best Conditions to Use

Thanks to Le Chatelier's principle (see page 27) you might think it would be easy to work out the optimum conditions for a reversible reaction. But in real life it's not quite that simple.

For most reversible reactions that are used on an industrial scale there are other factors, such as cost and time, that need to be taken into account.

Have a look at the conditions used for the production of _ethanol_ from _ethene_:

$$H_2C{=}CH_2(g) \; + \; H_2O(g) \underset{\text{endothermic}}{\overset{\text{exothermic}}{\rightleftharpoons}} CH_3CH_2OH(g)$$

Catalyst: H_3PO_4
Temperature: 300 °C
Pressure: 60 atm

Temperature:

1) <u>Lowering the temperature</u> would favour the forward reaction (see page 27), and so it should <u>increase the yield</u> of ethanol.
2) But lowering the temperature also means that fewer of the particles in the reaction mixture will have <u>enough energy to react</u>. So lowering the temperature will <u>slow down</u> both the forward and reverse reactions.
3) A low temperature would make the forward reaction too slow to be <u>useful</u>. So a <u>compromise temperature</u> of 300 °C is used.

Pressure:

1) <u>Increasing the pressure</u> would favour the forward reaction (see page 27), and increase the rate of reaction (as it increases the probability of collisions between particles). This would <u>increase the yield</u> of ethanol.
2) But producing high pressures uses a <u>lot of energy</u> and costs a <u>lot of money</u>. You'd need some pretty <u>strong</u> equipment to stand up to the high pressures too — and that would be expensive to buy and maintain.
3) To make the reaction economic, a moderately high <u>compromise pressure</u> of 60 atm is used.

Have a go at these questions on the conditions used in the production of ethanol from ethene:
1) Explain why it is not a good idea to run the reaction industrially at a temperature of 40 °C.
2) Explain why it is not a good idea to run the reaction industrially at a pressure of 500 atm.

Answers
1) The temperature is low, which would favour the forward reaction, and increase the yield of ethanol. But it is so low that the forward reaction rate will be much too slow to be economic.
2) The pressure is high, which would favour the forward reaction, and increase the yield of ethanol. But such a high pressure would be very expensive to maintain, making the reaction uneconomic.

Formulae of Compounds

Deducing the Formulae of Ionic Compounds

The formula of a compound tells you the _ratio_ of the elements that it contains. This ratio is fixed, and for ionic compounds that means it's easy to work out the formula from the charges on the ions.

Metal ions (and hydrogen ions) always carry a _positive charge_, whilst non-metal ions carry a _negative charge_. If you imagine that a positive charge is a 'hook' and a negative charge is an 'eye' then the formula can be deduced by exactly matching up the hooks and eyes. (This is to make the compound _electrically neutral_ — it's the same idea as the ionic lattices on page 10.)

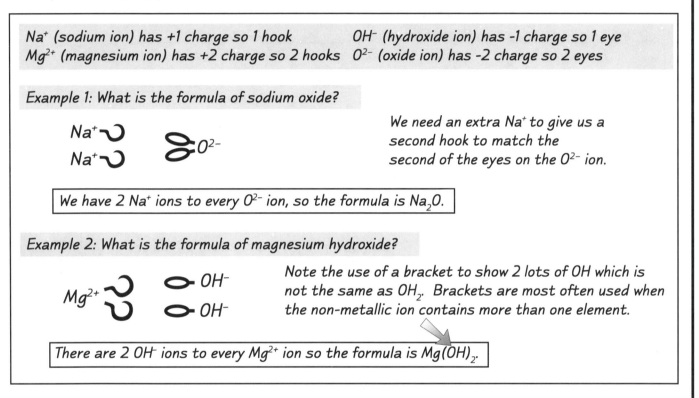

Na^+ (sodium ion) has +1 charge so 1 hook OH^- (hydroxide ion) has -1 charge so 1 eye
Mg^{2+} (magnesium ion) has +2 charge so 2 hooks O^{2-} (oxide ion) has -2 charge so 2 eyes

Example 1: What is the formula of sodium oxide?

Na^+
Na^+ O^{2-}

We need an extra Na^+ to give us a second hook to match the second of the eyes on the O^{2-} ion.

We have 2 Na^+ ions to every O^{2-} ion, so the formula is Na_2O.

Example 2: What is the formula of magnesium hydroxide?

Mg^{2+} OH^-
                   OH^-

Note the use of a bracket to show 2 lots of OH which is not the same as OH_2. Brackets are most often used when the non-metallic ion contains more than one element.

There are 2 OH^- ions to every Mg^{2+} ion so the formula is $Mg(OH)_2$.

Now try these:

Use the charges on the ions at the bottom of the box to deduce the formulae of the following ionic compounds.

1) sodium chloride
2) calcium bromide
3) sodium carbonate
4) aluminium oxide
5) iron(II) chloride

6) potassium oxide
7) aluminium chloride
8) potassium nitrate
9) aluminium sulfate
10) iron(III) nitrate

aluminium: Al^{3+} bromide: Br^- calcium: Ca^{2+} carbonate: CO_3^{2-}
chloride: Cl^- iron(II): Fe^{2+} iron(III): Fe^{3+} nitrate: NO_3^-
oxide: O^{2-} potassium: K^+ sodium: Na^+ sulfate: SO_4^{2-}

Answers

1) $NaCl$
2) $CaBr_2$
3) Na_2CO_3
4) Al_2O_3
5) $FeCl_2$
6) K_2O
7) $AlCl_3$
8) KNO_3
9) $Al_2(SO_4)_3$
10) $Fe(NO_3)_3$

Writing and Balancing Equations

Rules for Working out the Products Formed in Reactions

To write a balanced equation you need to be aware of the different ways that compounds react. Many examples involve the reactions of acids to form salts. It'll help you to know some of the rules for working out what products are formed during particular reactions.

<u>Making Salts</u>:

1. If <u>sulfuric acid</u> is used the salt will be a '_____' sulfate where '_____' is a metal.
   For example: copper + sulfuric acid = copper sulfate + hydrogen
2. If <u>hydrochloric acid</u> is used the salt will be a '_____' chloride where '_____' is a metal.
   For example: copper + hydrochloric acid = copper chloride + hydrogen
3. If <u>nitric acid</u> is used the salt will be a '_____' nitrate where '_____' is a metal.
   For example: copper + nitric acid = copper nitrate + hydrogen

(Sulfuric acid = H_2SO_4 Hydrochloric acid = HCl Nitric acid = HNO_3)

<u>Some Other General Rules</u>:

1. Combustion reactions result in the formation of oxides.
   For example: $2H_2 + O_2 \rightarrow 2H_2O$
2. When fuels burn, carbon dioxide (CO_2) and water (H_2O) are normally produced.
   For example: $C_5H_{12} + 8O_2 \rightarrow 5CO_2 + 6H_2O$
3. Atoms in gases often go round in pairs: H_2, N_2, O_2, Cl_2

<u>General Rules</u>
1. Always wear safety goggles
2. Be kind to animals
3. Wash behind your ears
4. No petting
5. Never trust a man with a number in his name

Writing Balanced Equations

To write a <u>balanced symbol equation</u> where you're given the reactants there are 5 simple steps:

1. Write out the <u>word equation</u> first.
2. Write the <u>correct formula</u> for each compound below its name (see page 29).
3. Go through each element in turn, making sure the <u>number of atoms</u> on each side of the equation <u>balances</u>.
4. If you changed any numbers, do step 3 again.
5. Keep doing this until all the elements balance.

<u>Doing the third step</u>:

If the atoms in the equation don't balance you can't change the molecular formulae — only the numbers in front of them.

For example:

$$CaO + 2HCl \rightarrow CaCl_2 + H_2O$$

There are two Cl on the right of the equation, so we need to have two HCl on the left-hand side. This also doubles the number of hydrogen atoms on the left-hand side, so that the hydrogens balance as well. This <u>always</u> works. If you can't get an equation to balance then it's <u>wrong</u>.

The example on the next page uses these rules to write a balanced symbol equation. Read through it carefully and make sure you understand the process.

Writing and Balancing Equations

Example: Write a balanced equation for the reaction of magnesium with hydrochloric acid.

Step 1: Magnesium + hydrochloric acid → magnesium chloride + hydrogen

Step 2: $Mg + HCl \rightarrow MgCl_2 + H_2$

Step 3: $Mg + 2HCl \rightarrow MgCl_2 + H_2$

(the Mgs already balance, put a 2 in front of HCl to balance the Hs and Cls. Check that all still balances.)

Now try this question:

1) Write a balanced symbol equation for the combustion of methane (CH_4) in oxygen. Step 1 has been done for you.

   Step 1: Methane + oxygen → carbon dioxide + water

Use everything that you've learnt on the last three pages to answer these questions:

2) Balance the symbol equations for the following reactions:
   a) $K + H_2SO_4 \rightarrow K_2SO_4 + H_2$
   b) $C_3H_8 + O_2 \rightarrow CO_2 + H_2O$
   c) $Na_2O + HCl \rightarrow NaCl + H_2O$
   d) $KOH + H_2SO_4 \rightarrow K_2SO_4 + H_2O$
3) Write balanced symbol equations for the following reactions.
   a) the complete combustion of the fuel ethanol (C_2H_5OH) in oxygen.
   b) the reaction of calcium hydroxide with hydrochloric acid to give calcium chloride and water.

chloride ion: Cl^- hydrogen ion: H^+ hydroxide ion: OH^- calcium ion: Ca^{2+}

Answers

1) Step 1: Methane + oxygen → carbon dioxide + water
   Step 2: $CH_4 + O_2 \rightarrow CO_2 + H_2O$
   Step 3: $CH_4 + 2O_2 \rightarrow CO_2 + 2H_2O$
   (The Cs already balance, so put a 2 in front of H_2O to balance the Hs. Now put a 2 in front of O_2 to balance the Os. Check that all still balances.)
2) a) $2K + H_2SO_4 \rightarrow K_2SO_4 + H_2$
   b) $C_3H_8 + 5O_2 \rightarrow 3CO_2 + 4H_2O$
   c) $Na_2O + 2HCl \rightarrow 2NaCl + H_2O$
   d) $2KOH + H_2SO_4 \rightarrow K_2SO_4 + 2H_2O$
3) a) $C_2H_5OH + 3O_2 \rightarrow 2CO_2 + 3H_2O$
   b) $Ca(OH)_2 + 2HCl \rightarrow CaCl_2 + 2H_2O$

Determination of Formulae from Reacting Masses

On page 29 you saw how to work out the formula of an ionic compound from the position of the reactants in the Periodic Table. Formulae are not always so easy to work out. Often, the only way to find out the formula of a compound is through _experimentation and calculation_.

The following three pages give explanations, examples and practice of the techniques used to find the formulae of various compounds. It will really help you to be comfortable with these methods, and able to do the calculations _quickly_.

Calculating Empirical Formulae

You can calculate the formula of a compound from the masses of the reactants.
Here is a simple set of rules to follow when calculating a formula:
1. Write the mass or percentage mass of each element
2. Divide by the relative atomic mass (A_r) of the atom
3. Divide all answers by the smallest answer
4. If required: multiply to make up to whole numbers
5. Use the ratio of atoms to write the formula (this gives the _empirical_ formula — see p.33)

Example: Find the formula of an oxide of aluminium formed from 9g aluminium and 8g oxygen.

Using the rules above:	Al	O
1. Write the mass of each element:	9g	8g
2. Divide by the relative atomic mass of each atom:	9/27	8/16
	= 0.333	= 0.5
3. Divide by the smallest answer:	0.333/0.333	0.5/0.333
	= 1	= 1.50
4. Make up to whole numbers (×2):	1×2 = 2	1.5×2 = 3
5. Use the ratio of atoms to write formula:	Al_2O_3	

Now try these questions:

1) Find the empirical formulae of the following three oxides of lead:
   - the first contains 12.94g of lead to every 1g of oxygen
   - the second comprises 6.47g of lead to every 1g of oxygen
   - the third contains 9.7g of lead to every 1g of oxygen
   (Relative atomic mass values: Pb = 207, O = 16)

2) Calculate the empirical formula of the carboxylic acid that is comprised of 4.3% hydrogen, 26.1% carbon and 69.6% oxygen.
   (Relative atomic mass values: H = 1, C = 12, O = 16)

Calculation of Empirical Formulae

Empirical and Molecular Formulae

The <u>empirical</u> formula of a compound is the simplest ratio of the atoms of each element in the compound.
The <u>molecular</u> formula of a compound gives the actual number of atoms of each element in the compound.
For example a compound with the molecular formula C_2H_6 has the empirical formula CH_3.
The <u>ratio</u> of the atoms is one C to every three Hs.

To find the molecular formula from the empirical formula, you need to know the <u>relative formula mass</u> (see page 3) of the compound. This will usually be given to you in the question. Read through the example below and then try the questions.

Calculating the molecular formula from the empirical formula:

Example: Calculate the molecular formula of a hydrocarbon molecule if the compound contains 85.7% carbon and it's relative formula mass is 42.

1. Calculate the empirical formula:

C	H
85.7	14.3
85.7/12	14.3/1
= 7.14	= 14.3
7.14/7.14	14.3/7.14
= 1	= 2
CH_2	

2. Calculate how many multiples of the empirical formula the molecular formula contains:

      1 empirical formula (CH_2) has a relative mass of 12 + 1 + 1 = 14
      The molecular formula has a relative mass of 42.
      42/14 = 3
      So the molecular formula is 3 × the empirical formula
          $C × 3 = 3C$, $H_2 × 3 = 6H$

   The molecular formula is: C_3H_6

Have a go at these:

1) Calculate the molecular formula of a compound containing 52.2% carbon, 13.0% hydrogen and 34.8% oxygen if the relative formula mass of the compound is 46.
(Relative atomic mass values: C = 12, H = 1, O = 16)

2) Calculate the molecular formula of a hydrocarbon with a relative formula mass of 78 that contains 92.3% carbon.
(Relative atomic mass values: C = 12, H = 1)

Determination of Formulae from Reacting Masses

More Practice Calculations

The more practice you get at these calculations the better. Be careful — some questions are asking you for the *empirical formula*, and some for the *molecular formula*.

Have a go at these:

1) What is the ratio of carbon to hydrogen atoms in a hydrocarbon molecule containing 75% carbon by mass?
(Relative atomic mass values: C = 12, H = 1)

2) What is the empirical formula of an oxide of nitrogen comprised of 30.4% nitrogen by mass?
(Relative atomic mass values: N = 14, O = 16)

3) What is the empirical formula of an oxide of sulfur if a 12g sample contains 6g of sulfur?
(Relative atomic mass values: S = 32, O = 16)

4) A compound of oxygen, titanium and iron contains 28% iron and 36% titanium.
What is the simplest formula of the compound?
(Relative atomic mass values: Fe = 55.8, Ti = 47.9, O = 16.0)

5) Calculate the molecular formula of an oxide of phosphorus that contains 0.775g of phosphorus to every 1g of oxygen and which has a relative formula mass of 284.
(Relative atomic mass values: P = 31, O = 16)

6) Calculate the molecular formula of aluminium chloride if it has 3.94g of chlorine to every 1g of aluminium, and a relative formula mass of 267.
(Relative atomic mass values: Al = 27, Cl = 35.5)

7) Calculate the molecular formula of titanium oxide if it contains one third oxygen by mass and has a relative formula mass of 144.
(Relative atomic mass values: Ti = 48, O = 16)

Making Use of the Periodic Table

The Periodic Table Holds Lots of Useful Information

From the _atomic number_ you can work out the _electronic configuration_ of an atom of the element.

The _mass number_ is the total number of protons and neutrons in the nucleus of one atom of an element.

The _first letter_ of the symbol is always a capital. If there is a second then it is lower case e.g. C, Na, K, Cl

This line marks the _boundary_ between _metals and non-metals_. All those elements to the right of it are non-metals.

Atomic number (or proton number) is the number of protons in the nucleus. This is also the number of electrons in an atom.

The _relative atomic mass_ is the _average mass number_ for all the _isotopes_ of an element, taking into account their relative abundance (see page 3).

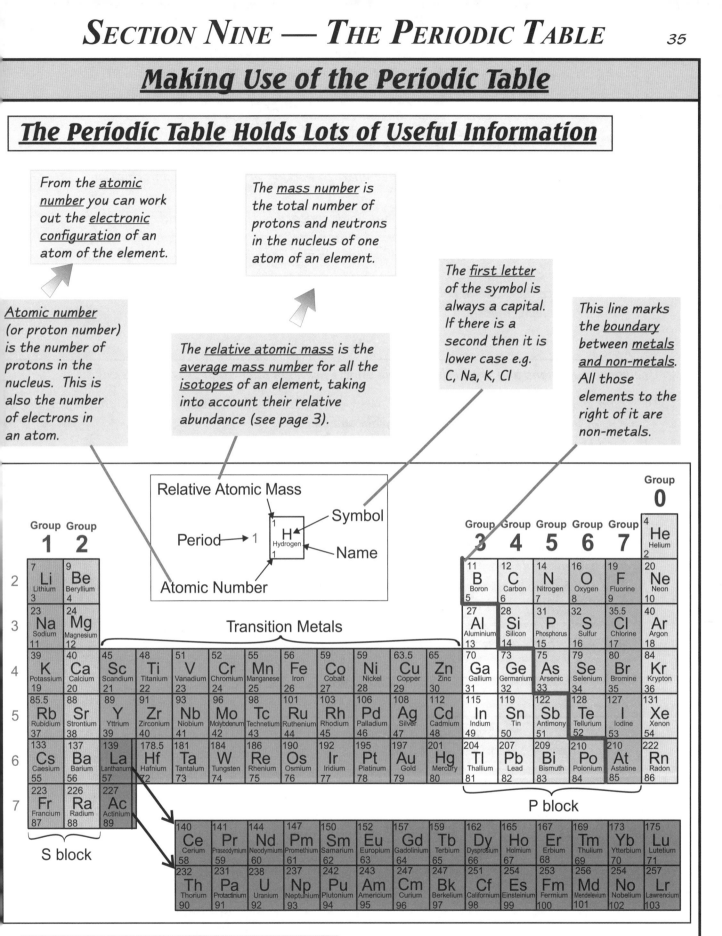

You can follow trends in physical and chemical properties down VERTICAL GROUPS and across HORIZONTAL PERIODS.

All elements in a group have the same _outer electron configuration_, and so form ions with the same charge. Knowing the number of electrons in the outer shell means you can work out the _formulae of compounds_.

Making Use of the Periodic Table

Learn and Practise Some Important Skills

You'll find chemistry heaps easier if you get used to working with the basic information that's contained in the Periodic Table.

1) One of the most important things that you can learn is the names and symbols of the elements — particularly the more common ones that you'll need to use a lot.

2) If you know the atomic number of an element in the Periodic Table, you can work out its electronic configuration.

3) Being able to do that will help you to work out the <u>formulae</u> of compounds, ionic or covalent, quickly.

Use these questions and the Periodic Table on the previous page to improve your skills.

1) Find the symbols or names of the following elements: calcium, vanadium, phosphorus, Br, tin, Au, W, potassium, manganese, boron, Sb, thallium.

2) Find the proton number for each of the elements in question 1.

3) Using only the proton number, write out the electronic configurations, using both crosses and the shorthand (2,8,4), for these elements: Na, S, Ca, N, Mg, He.

4) What is the charge on the ions formed by each of these elements: K, magnesium, nitrogen, sulfur, Al, I?

5) Work out the formulae of the following compounds: magnesium oxide, lithium bromide, aluminium sulfide, iron(II) oxide, copper(II) chloride.

6) Use the following information to predict the properties of bromine.
Fluorine is a highly reactive gas with a boiling point of −188 °C,
chlorine is a reactive gas with a boiling point of −35 °C,
iodine is a fairly unreactive solid with a boiling point of 184 °C.

223		75		96		14	
Fr		As		Mo		N	
African		Asian		Mammoth		Nellie	
87		33		42		7	

Reactivity and Group 2

Trend in Reactivity Down the Group

During their reactions, <u>Group 2 metals</u> donate their two outer electrons to another atom (usually a non-metal). The reactivity of Group 2 metals depends on how easily the outer electrons can be donated. The easier the electrons can be donated, the more reactive the metal will be. By experimenting, you can find that:

> Reactivity <u>increases</u> as you go <u>down</u> Group 2.

To see why this is, think about the factors that affect how strongly an electron is held by the nucleus:

1) The first is the <u>positive nuclear charge</u>. The nuclear charge attracts electrons and keeps them in orbit. A greater nuclear charge provides a <u>stronger</u> force of attraction and makes it more difficult for the atom to donate its outer electrons. As you go down the group, the nuclear charge increases, so if this was the only factor, reactivity would decrease down Group 2. But that isn't the case.

2) The second factor is that in larger atoms, the outer electrons are <u>further away</u> from the positive nucleus. The electrostatic attraction quickly <u>decreases</u> in strength with distance from the source.

3) The third factor is <u>electron shielding</u>. As the atoms in Group 2 get larger, the number of full electron shells round the nucleus increases. These negative charges shield the two outer electrons from the attraction of the positive nucleus.

The increase in the distance between the outer electrons and the nucleus, and the increased shielding as you go down the Group, far outweigh the increase in nuclear charge.

Trend in the Melting Points of Group 2 Metals

	Melting Point (°C)
Beryllium (Be)	1278
Magnesium (Mg)	651
Calcium (Ca)	839
Strontium (Sr)	769
Barium (Ba)	727

You can see from the table that:

> As you go <u>down</u> Group 2, melting point <u>decreases</u>.

Magnesium doesn't fit in with the general trend. It behaves a bit oddly because it has a slightly different structure to the other Group 2 metals.

This is also due to the increase in <u>electron shielding</u> as you go down the group.

Group 2 metals, like all other metals, are held together in a lattice structure by <u>metallic bonds</u>. Metallic bonds are formed when the outer electrons from each atom break free from the nucleus, leaving positive ions and <u>free electrons</u>.

The <u>strength</u> of the metallic bonds depend on how strong the attraction is between the positive ions and the free electrons. The more shielded the positive nuclei are, the weaker the attraction will be, and so the less energy will be required to break the bond and melt the metal.

Reactivity and Group 7

Some General Properties of Group 7 Elements

Group 7 elements all have 7 electrons in their outer shell.
As a result these elements either:

> 1)   Form ionic compounds by gaining an extra electron

or   2)   Share a pair of electrons and form a covalent bond

In their elemental state, the halogens bond covalently, forming _diatomic molecules_
(two atoms joined with a single covalent bond) with coloured vapours:

> _Chlorine_ (Cl_2) is a yellow/green gas at room temperature

> _Bromine_ (Br_2) is a brown liquid at room temperature

> _Iodine_ (I_2) is a grey solid at room temperature (which sublimes to produce a purple vapour)

In each case the atoms share an electron pair, as shown below:

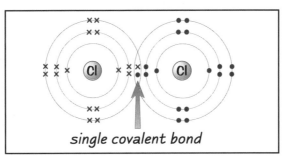

single covalent bond

As you go down the group:
1)   melting point increases
2)   boiling point increases

This is because the strength of the weak attraction between molecules
increases as the number of electrons in the molecules increase.

Trend in Reactivity Down Group 7

During their reactions, _Group 7 elements_ attract an extra electron from another atom.
The reactivity of Group 7 elements depends on how strongly the nucleus can attract electrons.
The stronger the attraction, the more reactive the element will be.

> Reactivity _decreases_ as you go _down_ Group 7.

The same arguments apply to the reactivity trend in the Group 7 elements as the one in Group 2.

1)   As with the Group 2 elements, _nuclear charge increases_ as you go _down_ the group.
     A greater nuclear charge will attract the extra electron required to fill the outer shell more
     strongly. This works to _increase_ the reactivity of the elements as you go down the group.

2)   However, as the atoms get bigger, the extra shells of electrons shield the nuclear charge
     more effectively. So the nucleus is less able to attract the extra electron the atom wants.

> In Group 7 this _shielding_ outweighs the effect of increasing nuclear charge. The elements
> at the top of the group are best able to attract an extra electron, and are more reactive.

Reactivity Trends in Groups 2 and 7

Group 7 Reactivity and Displacement Reactions

You can demonstrate the relative reactivity of the Group 7 elements using displacement reactions.

If you mix a halogen with a solution containing halide ions, a more reactive halogen will displace a less reactive halide ion (one below it in the group) from solution.

e.g. Fluorine is more reactive than chlorine.

$F_2 (aq) + 2Cl^- (aq) \rightarrow Cl_2 (aq) + 2F^- (aq)$

The chloride ions have been displaced from the solution.

Use the trends from the previous pages to answer the following questions:

1) The following are descriptions of the reactions of Be and Ca with cold water. Use them to predict the reactions of Mg and Sr.
   - Beryllium will not react with cold water at all
   - Calcium reacts steadily with cold water to produce hydrogen gas and calcium hydroxide.
2) Explain what would happen if you mixed the following halogens and halide solutions.
   a) chlorine and bromide
   b) bromine and iodide
   c) iodine and chloride
   d) iodine and bromide
   e) chlorine and iodide
3) For each of the reactions that takes place in question 2, write out an ionic equation.

Answers

1) Magnesium reacts very slowly with cold water to produce hydrogen gas and magnesium hydroxide.
   Strontium reacts vigorously with cold water to produce hydrogen gas and strontium hydroxide
2) a) Chlorine is more reactive than bromine, so it displaces the bromide in solution producing chloride and bromine.
   b) Bromine is more reactive than iodine, so it displaces the iodide in solution producing bromide and iodine.
   c) Iodine is less reactive than chlorine, so no reaction takes place.
   d) Iodine is less reactive than bromine, so no reaction takes place.
   e) Chlorine is more reactive than iodine, so it displaces the iodide in solution producing chloride and iodine.
3) $Cl_2 + 2Br^- \rightarrow 2Cl^- + Br_2$
   $Br_2 + 2I^- \rightarrow 2Br^- + I_2$
   $Cl_2 + 2I^- \rightarrow 2Cl^- + I_2$

Reaction Types

There are lots of types of <u>chemical reaction</u>. You will need to know all of them quite well. More importantly you need to be able to recognise when an individual reaction can be classed as more than one type. These pages give you types, explanations and examples (in alphabetical order).

Addition

This is a reaction in which atoms are added to an <u>unsaturated</u> bond so that the bond becomes <u>saturated</u>.

e.g.   ethene (C_2H_4) + H_2O → ethanol (C_2H_5OH)

Combustion

This is the chemical reaction between a <u>fuel</u> and <u>oxygen</u>. Normally the fuel is an organic compound and the products are <u>carbon dioxide</u> and <u>water</u>. Without enough oxygen, incomplete combustion takes place producing poisonous carbon monoxide (see page 20).

Condensation

This is similar to an <u>addition reaction</u> in which a simple molecule like <u>water</u> is also formed.

Cracking

This is the <u>(thermal) decomposition</u> of long-chain hydrocarbon molecules from crude oil into shorter- chain alkanes and alkenes. This requires high temperatures and pressures and a catalyst (usually aluminium oxide), and makes hydrocarbons that are more useful.

e.g.   decane $(C_{10}H_{22})$ → octane (C_8H_{18}) + ethene (C_2H_4)

Dehydration

This is the <u>removal of water</u> from a compound by <u>heating</u>.
In organic molecules it usually results in the formation of a C=C bond.

e.g.   ethanol (C_2H_5OH) → ethene (C_2H_4) + H_2O

Displacement

This is a reaction where one element displaces another, <u>less reactive</u>, element from a compound. This usually takes place between metals, but also with halogens.

e.g. $2Al(s)$ + $Fe_2O_3(s)$ → $Al_2O_3(s)$ + $2Fe(s)$ (the Thermite Reaction)

Disproportionation

This is a rare type of chemical reaction where an element in a reactant is <u>oxidised</u> and <u>reduced</u> at the same time. <u>Chlorine</u> can undergo disproportionation reactions.

e.g. $Cl_2(aq)$ + $H_2O(l)$ → $HOCl(aq)$ + $HCl(aq)$
                  Chloric(I) acid   Hydrochloric acid

The chlorine has been: <u>oxidised</u>   <u>reduced</u>

Reaction Types

Electrolysis

This is a process that uses _electricity_ to _break down_ a compound. The reactant or reactants must be in the _liquid_ state — either molten or in solution. The particles have to be able to move. The name can be split into two bits: 'electro-' for electricity and '-lysis' means to break down. An example is the electrolysis of bauxite to obtain pure aluminium.

Elimination

This is just _the removal of a small molecule from a larger molecule_.
Usually H_2O or H_2 is removed (and not replaced by anything else).

Endothermic

Any chemical reaction that _takes in heat_ energy.
This means that the reactants will have less energy than the products.

Exothermic

Any chemical reaction that _gives out heat_ energy. This happens because the products have less energy than the reactants. Hint: 'exo-' and 'exit' come from the same word meaning 'out'.

Hydrogenation

This is the _addition_ of a molecule of hydrogen (H_2) across a C=C bond.
One atom attaches to each carbon.

e.g.   ethene (C_2H_4) + H_2 → ethane (C_2H_6)

Neutralisation

This is the reaction between a _basic_ compound and an _acid_. The products always include the _salt_ of the acid, _water_ and other products dependent on the acid and base.

e.g. $2KOH(aq) + H_2SO_4(aq) \rightarrow K_2SO_4(aq) + 2H_2O(l)$
$Na_2CO_3(aq) + 2HCl(aq) \rightarrow 2NaCl(aq) + CO_2(g) + H_2O(l)$

Oxidation

There are two possible definitions for this; the best is the _loss of electrons_.
Another useful one is the _gain of oxygen_. It is the opposite of reduction.

Precipitation

A precipitate is a _solid_ that is formed in a solution by a chemical reaction or by a change in temperature affecting solubility. Precipitates are _insoluble_ in the solvent.
A precipitation reaction is simply any reaction that produces a precipitate.

Reaction Types

REDOX

This is the name for a reaction that involves both _reduction_ and _oxidation_ processes.
It is usually used to describe reactions that just involve electron transfer.

e.g.
$$Fe(s) + Cu^{2+}(aq) \rightarrow Fe^{2+}(aq) + Cu(s)$$
reduction

oxidation

Reduction

There are two possible definitions for this; the best is the _gain of electrons_.
The other useful one is the _loss of oxygen_. Important point: oxidation and reduction
ALWAYS happen together — it is impossible to have one without the other.

Reversible

This is the name given to any chemical reaction that can go _forwards and backwards_
at the same time. That means that the reactants will form the products, but that
the products will also react (or decompose) to give the reactants.

e.g.
$$N_2(g) + 3H_2(g) \rightleftharpoons 2NH_3(g)$$

Substitution

This is simply a reaction in which an atom (or group of atoms) in a molecule
are _swapped_ for a different atom (or group of atoms).

Thermal Decomposition

This is where one compound breaks down, under heating, into two or more simpler compounds.
A classic example is the breakdown of any _carbonate compound_,

e.g.
$$CaCO_3 \xrightarrow{heat} CaO + CO_2$$

Cracking of hydrocarbons is also an example.

Now try these questions:

Write down all the different types of reaction that each of the following could be classed as.

1) burning ethanol
2) iron + copper sulfate → iron sulfate + copper
3) hydrochloric acid + sodium hydroxide → sodium chloride + water (gets hotter)
4) propene (C_3H_6) + H_2 → propane (C_3H_8)

Exothermic and Endothermic Reactions

In an <u>exothermic</u> reaction, heat energy is given out (the room temperature rises).
In an <u>endothermic</u> reaction, heat energy is taken from the surroundings (the room temperature drops).

Making and Breaking Bonds

When two atoms joined by a covalent bond are <u>separated</u>, the energy required
to do this must be provided from the surroundings. Reactions which require an
<u>energy input</u> like this are called <u>endothermic</u> reactions.
When two atoms become <u>joined</u> together by forming a covalent bond, energy is
released to the surroundings. Reactions that <u>release energy</u> to the
surroundings are called <u>exothermic</u> reactions.

Reactions can be Represented by Energy Level Diagrams

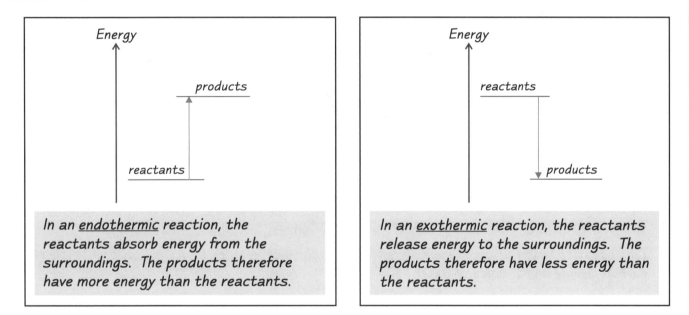

In an <u>endothermic</u> reaction, the
reactants absorb energy from the
surroundings. The products therefore
have more energy than the reactants.

In an <u>exothermic</u> reaction, the reactants
release energy to the surroundings. The
products therefore have less energy than
the reactants.

Have a go at these questions:

Are the following reactions exothermic or endothermic?

1) photosynthesis (uses energy from sunlight)
2) respiration
3) burning coal
4) sodium hydrogencarbonate + hydrochloric acid (temperature drops)
5) acid + hydroxide (gets hotter)
6) methane + steam (cools as they react)

<u>Answers</u>
1) Endothermic
2) Exothermic
3) Exothermic
4) Endothermic
5) Exothermic
6) Endothermic

Calculations Involving Making and Breaking Bonds

Average Bond Energy

Bonds between different atoms require different amounts of energy to break them. When the same two atoms bond in the same way, the amount of energy needed is always about the same. The average bond energy values for some common bonds are given below:

C — H	413		C — O	360		C = C	612
O = O	498		H — H	436		C = O	743
C — C	348		O — H	463			

All values are in kJmol^{-1} (that means the same as kJ/mol).

The values tell you that:

e.g. It takes 413 kJ of energy to break 1 mole of C — H bonds.
It takes 463 × 2 = 926 kJ to break 1 mole of water (which has 2 O — H bonds per molecule) into oxygen and hydrogen atoms.
743 × 2 = 1486 kJ are released when 1 mole of CO_2 (which has 2 C = O bonds) forms.

Calculating the Change in Energy

When a reaction takes place, the change in energy is simply:

sum of energy required to break old bonds – sum of energy released by new bonds formed

---

Example: Calculate the energy change involved when 1 mole of methane burns in oxygen.

$$CH_4 \ + \ 2O_2 \ \rightarrow \ CO_2 \ + \ 2H_2O$$

(The equation tells you that 1 mole of methane reacts with 2 moles of oxygen to form 1 mole of carbon dioxide and 2 moles of water.)

Solution:

Step 1: Calculate the energy required to break all of the bonds between the reactant atoms

4 C — H bonds	=	4 × 413	= 1652 kJ
2 O = O bonds	=	2 × 498	= 996 kJ
		TOTAL	= 2648 kJ

Remember — there are 2 moles of oxygen

Step 2: Calculate the energy released by all the new bonds formed between the atoms in the products

2 C = O bonds	=	2 × 743	= 1486 kJ
4 O — H bonds	=	4 × 463	= 1852 kJ
		TOTAL	= 3338 kJ

1 mole of CO_2 is formed and 2 moles of H_2O

Step 3: Combine the two values to give an overall value for the energy change

The overall energy change combines +2648 and –3338 which equals –690 kJmol^{-1}

The negative sign shows that energy is being <u>released</u> to the surroundings, indicating that this is an <u>exothermic</u> reaction. This is what you would expect, since this is a combustion reaction.

Calculations Involving Making and Breaking Bonds

Calculate how much energy is released in the following reactions:

1) burning 1 mole of propane $C_3H_8 + 5O_2 \rightarrow 3CO_2 + 4H_2O$
2) burning 1 mole of ethanol $C_2H_5OH + 3O_2 \rightarrow 2CO_2 + 3H_2O$
3) burning 1 mole of octane $C_8H_{18} + 12\frac{1}{2}O_2 \rightarrow 8CO_2 + 9H_2O$
4) hydrogenation of 1 mole of ethene $C_2H_4 + H_2 \rightarrow C_2H_6$

Answers

1) Step 1: Calculate the energy required to break all the bonds between the reactant atoms
8 C — H bonds   =   8 × 413 = 3304
2 C — C bonds   =   2 × 348 = 696
5 O = O bonds   =   5 × 498 = 2490
TOTAL = 6490

Step 2: Calculate the energy released by all the new bonds formed between the product atoms
6 C = O bonds   =   6 × 743 = 4458
8 O — H bonds   =   8 × 463 = 3704
TOTAL = 8162

Step 3: Combine the two values to give an overall value for the energy change
+6490 − 8162 = −1672 kJmol⁻¹

2) Step 1: Calculate the energy required to break all of the bonds between the reactant atoms
1 C — C bond   =   1 × 348 = 348
1 C — O bond   =   1 × 360 = 360
5 C — H bonds   =   5 × 413 = 2065
1 O — H bond   =   1 × 463 = 463
3 O = O bonds   =   3 × 498 = 1494
TOTAL = 4730

Step 2: Calculate the energy released by all the new bonds formed between the product atoms
4 C = O bonds   =   4 × 743 = 2972
6 O — H bonds   =   6 × 463 = 2778
TOTAL = 5750

Step 3: Combine the two values to give an overall value for the energy change
+4730 − 5750 = −1020 kJmol⁻¹

3) Step 1: Calculate the energy required to break all of the bonds between the reactant atoms
18 C — H bonds   =   18 × 413 = 7434
7 C — C bonds   =   7 × 348 = 2436
12.5 O = O bonds   =   12.5 × 498 = 6225
TOTAL = 16 095

Step 2: Calculate the energy released by all the new bonds formed between the product atoms
16 C = O bonds   =   16 × 743 = 11 888
18 O — H bonds   =   18 × 463 = 8334
TOTAL = 20 222

Step 3: Combine the two values to give an overall value for the energy change
+16 095 − 20 222 = −4127 kJmol⁻¹

4) Step 1: Calculate the energy required to break the H — H and C = C bonds
1 H — H bond   =   1 × 436 = 436
1 C = C bond   =   1 × 612 = 612
TOTAL = 1048

Step 2: Calculate the energy released by all the new bonds formed between product atoms
2 C — H bonds   =   2 × 413 = 826
1 C — C bond   =   1 × 348 = 348
TOTAL = 1174

Step 3: Combine the two values to give an overall value for the energy change
+1048 − 1174 = −126 kJmol⁻¹

Evaluating Data

Evidence is Reliable if it Can be Repeated

Scientific evidence needs to be reliable (or reproducible). If it isn't, then it doesn't really help you.

When you're doing an investigation, you need to repeat your experiment several times to <u>make sure</u> your results are reliable — you should get round about the same answer each time.

<u>RELIABLE</u> *means the results can be consistently reproduced in independent experiments.*

Example: Cold Fusion.

In 1989, two scientists claimed that they'd produced 'cold fusion' (the energy source from the Sun at room temperature). It was huge news — if true, it could have meant clean energy from sea water. But other scientists just couldn't get the same results — they weren't reliable. And until they are, the scientific community won't take cold fusion seriously.

Repeating an Experiment Lets You Find a Mean Result

If you repeat an experiment, your results will usually be slightly different each time you do it. You can use the mean (or average) of the measurements to represent all these values. The more times you repeat the experiment the more reliable the average will be. To find the mean:

<u>ADD TOGETHER</u> *all the data values then <u>DIVIDE</u> by the total number of values in the sample.*

Example: The rate of reaction between hydrochloric acid and magnesium metal.

You're doing the rate of reaction experiment shown on page 24. You repeat it three times to check your results are reliable. You get these results for the volume of gas given off after 30 seconds.

Run 1	Run 2	Run 3	Mean
23 cm³	22 cm³	25 cm³	**23.3 cm³**

$\Longleftarrow (23 + 22 + 25) \div 3 = 23.3 \text{ cm}^3$

Watch out for weird results that stick out like a hedgehog in a tea cup. These are called <u>anomalous</u> results. Think about what's likely to have caused them. For example — if one of the results above was only 5 cm³, then something probably went wrong. Maybe the plunger got stuck. You should ignore the anomalous result when you calculate the mean.

Repeating experiments may not make your data more accurate. For instance, if your balance always reads 2 grams below the actual mass, repeating the measurements won't make it any more accurate.

Evidence Also Needs to be Valid

Collecting reliable data is important, but if the data doesn't answer your original question, it won't be any use. You need to think about <u>what</u> data to collect to make sure your results will be valid.

<u>VALID</u> *means that the data is reliable <u>AND</u> answers the original question.*

To answer scientific questions, scientists often try to link changes in one variable with another. For your data to be valid, you have to control all the other variables...

Evaluating Data

You Need to Control All the Variables

Scientists control the variables so that the only one that changes is the one they're investigating — all the others are kept constant. If one variable changes when another variable does, the variables are said to be _correlated_.

> Example: The effect of surface area on reaction rate.
>
> If you're investigating the effect of surface area on the rate of reaction you have to keep everything else, such as temperature and concentration, exactly the same. Surface area is the only variable that you change.

In experiments like this, you can say that one variable _causes_ the other one to change because you have made sure that nothing else could be causing the change.

Controlling All the Variables Is Often Really Hard

The difficulty with a lot of scientific investigations is that it's very hard to control all the variables that might (just might) be having an effect.

> Example: Investigating whether chlorinated water increases cancer risk.
>
> Some studies claim that drinking chlorinated tap water increases the risk of certain cancers. But it's hard to control all the variables between people who drink tap water and people who don't. So designing a fair test is very tricky.

Even if some studies do show that people who drink more chlorinated water are slightly more likely to get certain cancers, it _doesn't_ mean that drinking chlorinated water _causes_ cancer. There will be heaps of differences between the groups of people. It could be due to any of them.

Correlation _DOESN'T_ always mean cause

Watch Out For Bias

People who want to make a point sometimes present data in a _biased_ way to suit their own purposes. They don't necessarily lie, they might just use the bits of data that support their argument, or phrase things in a leading way.

There are loads of reasons they might want to do this — for example, a company that sells water filters might tell you about the studies that found a link between drinking chlorinated water and cancer, and forget to mention all the studies that didn't find a link. They'll sell more water filters if people think drinking tap water isn't safe.

Benefits and Risks Must be Weighed Up

Scientific discoveries are often really useful, and they've improved our lives no end. But they often have risks attached. Society has to weigh things up and decide if they want to take the risks to get the benefits.

> Example: Adding chlorine to drinking water.
>
> Even if chlorine in water can cause health risks, these are extremely small compared to the risk of getting a nasty disease from drinking water with bacteria in.

Index

A

activation energy 25
addition 40
alkanes 13, 21, 40
alkenes 22, 40
anions 9
atomic number 2, 6, 35
atoms 1-4
average bond energy 44
average mass number 3, 35
averaging results 46

B

balanced symbol equations 30-31
bias 47
boiling points 11, 13-15, 21, 38
bonding pairs 14

C

calculating empirical formulae 32
carbon 8, 13, 15, 19-20
carbon dioxide 20, 24, 30, 40
carbon monoxide 20, 40
carbonates 9, 24, 42
catalysts 25
cations 9
charge 1, 9-10, 29
chlorine 2-3, 7, 10-11, 38, 40
combustion 20, 30, 40
complete combustion 20
condensation 40
covalent compounds
        8, 13-17, 21-22, 38
cracking 25, 40, 42
crude oil 19, 40

D

dehydration 40
diamond 15
diatomic molecules 38
displacement 39-40
disproportionation 40

E

electrical conductivity 11, 14, 16
electrolysis 41
electron arrangement 5
electron pairs 8, 14, 38
electron shielding 37-38
electrons 1-2, 5-9, 35, 37-38
elements 2-3, 6-7, 9, 17, 35-39
elimination 41
empirical formula 32-33
endothermic 27-28, 41, 43
energy level diagrams 43

energy levels 5-6
equilibrium 26-28
exothermic 20, 27-28, 41, 43-44

F

formulae 29, 32-33, 35-36
fractional distillation 19
free electrons 15, 37
fuels 20

G

giant covalent structures 15-16
giant ionic structures 10-11
graphite 15-16
Group 2 metals 9, 37
Group 7 elements 9, 38-39

H

halogens 38-39
hydrocarbons 13-14, 19-22, 40
hydrogen
        8, 13-14, 19, 21-22, 24, 30, 41
hydrogen bonds 14
hydrogenation 41

I

incomplete combustion 20, 40
ionic compounds
        7-8, 10-11, 17, 29, 38
ions 1-2, 7, 9-11, 29, 35, 39
isomers 22
isotopes 2, 3, 35

L

Le Chatelier's Principle 27-28
lone pairs 14

M

macromolecules 15-16
mass number 2-3, 35
melting points 11, 15, 17, 37, 38
metallic bonds 37
metals 8, 35, 37
molar mass 4
mole 4, 44
molecular formulae 33-34
monomers 23

N

neutralisation 24, 41
neutrons 1, 2, 35
noble gas electronic structures 9
non-polar molecules 14

nuclear charge 37-38
nucleus 1-2, 9, 35, 37-38

O

oxidation 41
oxidation states 9
oxides 17, 29-30

P

'p' block 6
'p' level 5-6
percentage mass 32-33
Periodic Table 3, 6, 17, 35-36
polar molecules 11, 13-14
polymers 21-23
position of equilibrium 27
precipitation 24, 41
protons 1, 2, 35

R

reaction rates 24-26, 28
reactivity trends 37-39
REDOX 42
reduction 42
relative abundance 3, 35
relative atomic mass (A_r) 3-4, 32-35
relative formula mass (M_r) 3-4, 33
relative molecular mass 3
reliability 46
reversible reactions 26-28

S

's' block 6
's' level 5-6
salts 30
small covalent molecules 8, 13-14, 17
sodium chloride 7, 10-11
solubility 11, 14, 16
substitution 42

T

thermal decomposition 42
transition metals 9

V

validity 46
variables 47
viscosity 21
volatility 21

Y

yield 26-28